BRAIN ACADEMY
SUPERMATHS

CW00418514

Louise Moore, Pete Crawford
and Richard Cooper

Mission File 2
Years 3-4

roduced in association with

n a c e

National Association
for Able Children
in Education

RISING STARS

Rising Stars are grateful to the following people for their support in developing this series: Sue Mordecai, Julie Fitzpatrick, Johanna Raffan, Belle Wallace and Clive Tunnicliffe.

NACE, PO Box 242, Arnolds Way, Oxford OX2 9FR
www.nace.co.uk

Rising Stars UK Ltd, 22 Grafton Street, London W1S 4EX
www.risingstars-uk.com

Every effort has been made to trace copyright holders and obtain their permission for the use of copyright materials. The authors and publisher will gladly receive information enabling them to rectify any error or omission in subsequent editions.

All facts are correct at time of going to press.

Published 2007
Text, design and layout © Rising Stars UK Ltd.

Editorial Consultant: Jean Carnall
Cover design: Burville-Riley
Design: Pentacor**big**
Illustrations: Cover Burville-Riley / Characters – Bill Greenhead

British Library Cataloguing in Publication Data.
A CIP record for this book is available from the British Library.

ISBN: 978-1-84680-231-7

Printed by Craft Print International Ltd, Singapore

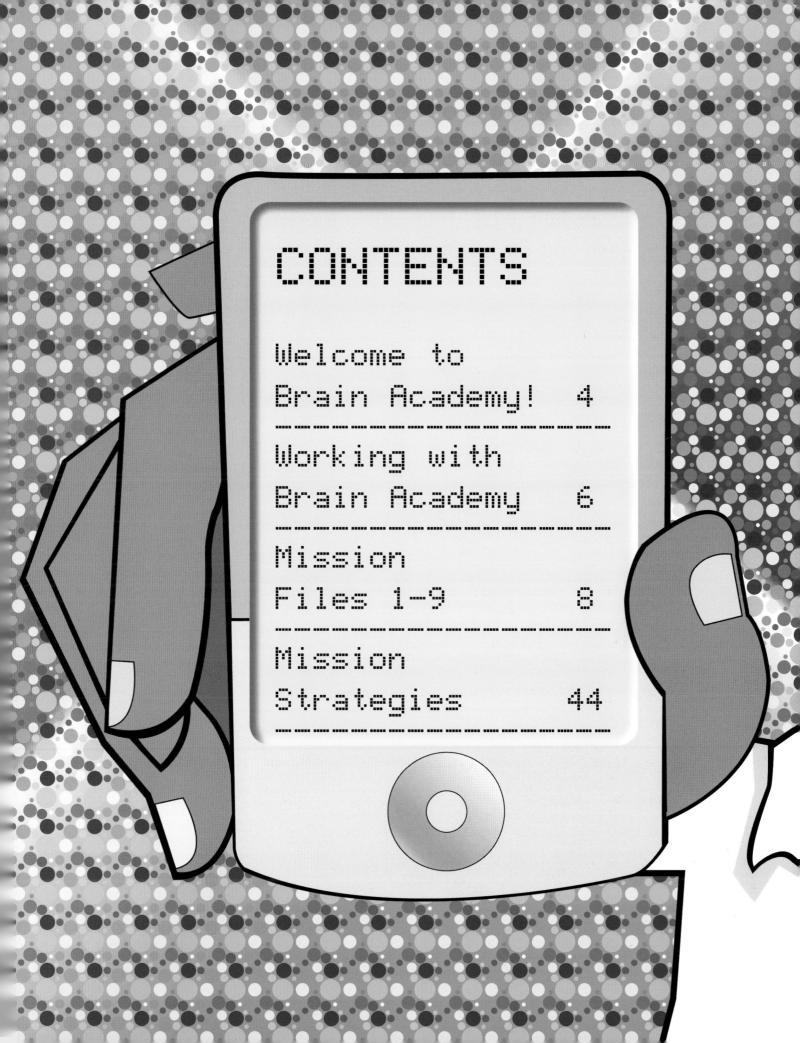

CONTENTS

Welcome to Brain Academy!

Welcome to Brain Academy! Make yourself at home. We are here to give you the low-down on the organisation – so pay attention!

It's our job to help Da Vinci and his colleagues to solve the tough problems they face and we would like you to join us as members of the Academy. Are you up to the challenge?

Da Vinci

Da Vinci is the founder and head of the Brain Academy. He is all seeing, all thinking and all knowing – possibly the cleverest person alive. Nobody has ever actually seen him in the flesh as he communicates only via computer. When Da Vinci receives an emergency call for help, the members of Brain Academy jump into action (and that means you!).

Huxley

Huxley is Da Vinci's right-hand man. Not as clever, but still very smart. He is here to guide you through the missions and offer help and advice. The sensible and reliable face of Brain Academy, Huxley is cool under pressure.

Dr Hood

The mad doctor is the arch-enemy of Da Vinci and Brain Academy. He has set up a rival organisation called D.A.F.T. (which stands for Dull And Feeble Thinkers). Dr Hood and his agents will do anything they can to irritate and annoy the good people of this planet. He is a pain we could do without.

Hilary Kumar

Ms Kumar is the Prime Minister of our country. As the national leader she has a hotline through to the Academy but will only call in an extreme emergency. Confident and strong willed, she is a very tough cookie indeed.

General Cods-Wallop

This highly decorated gentleman (with medals, not wallpaper) is in charge of the armed forces. Most of his success has come from the help of Da Vinci and the Academy rather than the use of his somewhat limited military brain.

Mrs Tiggles

Stella Tiggles is the retired head of the Secret Intelligence service. She is a particular favourite of Da Vinci who treats her as his own mother. Mrs Tiggles' faithful companion is her cat, Bond… James Bond.

We were just like you once – ordinary schoolchildren leading ordinary lives. Then one day we all received a call from a strange character named Da Vinci. From that day on, we have led a double life – as secret members of Brain Academy!

Here are a few things you should know about the people you'll meet on your journey.

Inspector Pattern
The trusty Inspector is Buster's right-hand lady. Ms Pattern looks for clues in data and is the complete opposite to the muddled D.A.F.T. agents. Using her mathematical mind to find order where there is chaos, she is a welcome addition to Da Vinci's team. In fact some of the team would do well to think in such a methodical way... a certain Mr Blastov perhaps?

Maryland T. Wordsworth
M.T. Wordsworth is the president of the USA. Not the sharpest tool in the box, Maryland prefers to be known by his middle name, Texas, or 'Tex' for short. He takes great exception to being referred to as 'Mary' (which has happened in the past).

Buster Crimes
Buster is a really smooth dude and is in charge of the Police Force. His laid-back but efficient style has won him many friends, although these don't include Dr Hood or the agents of D.A.F.T. who regularly try to trick the coolest cop in town.

Sandy Buckett
The fearless Sandy Buckett is the head of the fire service. Sandy and her team of brave firefighters are always on hand, w er to extinguish the flames of chaos caused by the demented Dr Hood or just to rescue Mrs Tiggles' cat...

Echo the Eco-Warrior
Echo is the hippest chick around. Her love of nature and desire for justice will see her do anything to help an environmental cause – even if it means she's going to get her clothes dirty.

Prince Barrington
Prince Barrington, or 'Bazza' as he is known to his friends, is the publicity-seeking heir to the throne. Always game for a laugh, the Prince will stop at nothing to raise money for worthy causes. A 'good egg' as his mother might say.

Victor Blastov

Victor Blastov is the leading scientist at the Space Agency. He once tried to build a rocket by himself but failed to get the lid off the glue. Victor often requires the services of the Academy, even if it's to set the video to record Dr Who.

Working with Brain Academy

Do you get the idea? Now you've had the introduction we are going to show you the best way to use this book.

MISSION FILE 2:6

Time flies (if you throw your watch out of the window!)

Time: Morning has broken
Place: Army barracks

Two new recruits are arriving at the army – Private Sloppy (PS) and Private Joker (PJ).

It's important we get everything on time, by Jove. I need to know that my recruits are following a tight schedule.

We'll need to lend the General a hand. I have a sneaky suspicion about these two …

TM

Hmmm. Who do you think they might be working for? Let's try to find out more.

1) PJ takes 2 hours longer to travel to base than PS. Both leave home after 8 a.m. and arrive at the base at 4 p.m. They both leave home on the hour.

What times might they have left home? Work out all the possible answers.

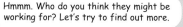
Just keep adding 1 hour at a time.

28

TM

2) The new recruits register. It takes PS 9 minutes and PJ 15 minutes. Next, they both make a phone call home.

PS is on the phone 4 minutes less than PJ. PS spends at least 5 minutes on the phone.

a) If PJ talks on the phone for 20 minutes, how long does it take PS to register and phone?

b) What is the least time they could each spend registering and phoning?

3) When they are shown to their rooms, they have to unpack. Then, they make up their beds.

It takes PJ 3 times as long to make up his bed as it does to unpack.

It takes PS twice as long to unpack as to make up his bed.

a) If they both take 10 minutes to unpack, how long does it take each of them to make up their bed?

b) If they both take exactly 36 minutes to unpack and make up their bed, how long does each recruit spend on each activity?

29

The plot
This tells you what the mission is about.

The Training Mission
Huxley will give you some practice before sending you on the main mission.

Each mission is divided up into different parts.

6

Each book contains a number of 'missions' for you to take part in. You will work with the characters in Brain Academy to complete these missions.

Huxley's Think Tank

Huxley will give you some useful tips to help you on each mission.

The Main Mission

This is where you try to complete the challenge.

MM

In the morning, the new recruits do the same jobs in the same order. Work out at what time they do each job.

1) They both get up at 6 a.m.

PJ takes 4 minutes longer to shower than PS. Both brush their teeth for 3 minutes.

PS took twice as long to dress as to shower. PJ took the same length of time to do both.

PJ made his bed in 3 minutes. This was half the time PS took.

They both spend 10 minutes preparing the room for inspection. PS spends at least 2 minutes in the shower.

a) What is the earliest they could each be ready?

HUXLEY'S THINK TANK

- You could work from how long PS spent in the shower.

MM

b) How long does PS spend in the shower if they are both ready at the same time?

c) If they are both ready by 7 a.m., find all the possible times they could be ready.

d) For a special mission, they have to be ready at 5:12 a.m. exactly. If it takes PJ 9 minutes to dress, what time should they each get up to make sure they are ready in time?

Da Vinci Files

Make up your own problem involving different lengths of time. Make sure that:

- you keep at least one of the lengths of time secret.
- one of your other times is a given length of time more or less than the missing length of time.
- you give either a start or finish time.
- there are at least 4 activities that have to be timed.

Ask a friend to solve your problem to check it works.

Just as I thought, General. Those two are D.A.F.T. agents in disguise!

Great Scott! How do you know?

I overheard PJ say that there are 3 kinds of people in this world – those that can count and those that can't!

30

31

No one said this was easy. In fact, that is why you have been chosen. Da Vinci will only take the best and he believes that includes you. Good luck!

PS: See pages 44–47 for some hints and tips and a useful process.

The Da Vinci Files

These problems are for the best Brain Academy recruits. Very tough. Are you tough enough?

Piping problem for Sandy

Time: First thing
Place: The fire station

Sandy Bucket is replacing the metal pipes on a pump in the fire engine. She has several boxes containing small pieces of pipe that can fit together. However, not everything is going to plan...

Arghh! These pipes are really, really annoying! Huxley, can you and the team lend a hand?

Pipe down, Ms Buckett, not so loud! Of course we can.

TM

Sandy found a box that contained these 6 pieces of pipe. The number on each piece shows its length. The pieces can be joined together to make different lengths of pipe.

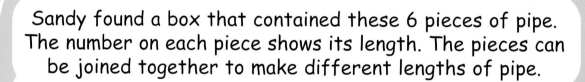

| 1 | 2 | 4 | 5 |

| 7 | 9 |

1) What pieces can Sandy use to make a pipe

   a) with length 6?   **b) with length 12?**

2) What is the shortest pipe she could have?

What is the longest?

3) Sandy found this set of pipes in another box.

(1) (2) (3) (4)

This is how she made
a length 10 pipe.

(4 | 3 | 2 | 1)

She found 2 ways of making
a length 5 pipe.

(2 | 3)

(1 | 4)

Sandy decided to make a table showing the ways she could make all the lengths between 1 and 10. Here is the start of her table.

Length 1	
Length 2	
Length 3	
Length 4	
Length 5	2 + 3, 1 + 4
Length 6	
Length 7	
Length 8	
Length 9	
Length 10	1 + 2 + 3 + 4

Copy and complete the table, finding as many ways as you can for making each length.

I love pipes – bagpipes, that is. How do you tell if a bagpipe is out of tune?

Easy, someone is blowing into it!

1) Sandy found another box that contained these 4 pieces of pipe.

| 1 | 2 | 5 | 9 |

a) What is the shortest pipe she can make using these pieces?

b) What is the longest pipe she can make?

c) Find out if Sandy can make ALL the lengths between the shortest and longest with this set of pipes.

Keep a record of all the lengths you find. You might discover more than one way of making some of them.

2) Make your own set of 4 pipes that will let you make every length between 1 and the longest possible length.

Can you find a set that gives you more lengths than Sandy's?

3) What is the longest length you can make when all the pipes are put together? Make sure you can still make all the lengths between 1 and the longest.

HUXLEY'S THINK TANK

- You could use cubes to make the different lengths of pipe.
- Write a list of all the lengths between the shortest and longest to help you keep track of the lengths you can make.

Thanks guys, your plumbing skills were piping hot!

Da Vinci files

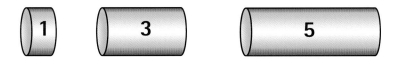

| 1 | 3 | 5 |
| 6 | 10 | |

- What is the shortest length Sandy can make using these pieces? What is the longest?
- Find out if she can make all the lengths between the shortest and longest with this set of pipes.

  Keep a record of all these lengths and the ways of making them.

- Make your own set of 5 pipes that will let you make every length between 1 and the longest possible length. Try to make it so that it gives the longest pipe that you can!

Tessa, late?
No, she made it just in time!

Time: For a new driveway
Place: Barrington Hall

Prince Barrington wants unique designs for his huge driveway at Barrington Hall. The stones in the path must tessellate but have different numbers of sides. He likes to set a challenge, does our Prince!

Your task is to present designs that are original and exciting for the monarch to be.

> We must make sure we go down the correct path with our designs.

> Hmmm. No more 'path'-etic jokes please, young man.

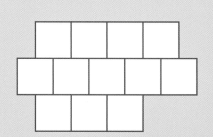

> First of all, you need to investigate which shapes will tessellate. Shapes that tessellate fit together without leaving any gaps between. Here are two different tessellations using squares.

1) See if you can make each of these shapes tessellate.
   If so, how many tessellating patterns can you make?

a)

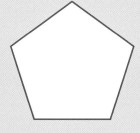

regular pentagon

b)

equilateral triangle

c)

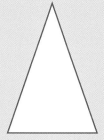

isosceles triangle

d)

scalene triangle

e)

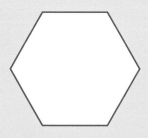

regular hexagon

f)

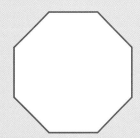

regular octagon

2) Did all the regular shapes tessellate?

Did any irregular shapes tessellate?

HUXLEY'S THINK TANK

- Regular shapes have sides
  that are all the same length.

I really want octagonal tiles that tessellate. Any ideas?

1) Use a square piece of card.

Cut a triangle from one side like this.

Stick the triangle on the opposite side.

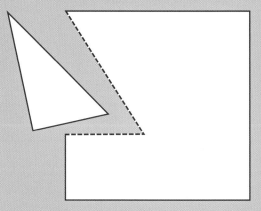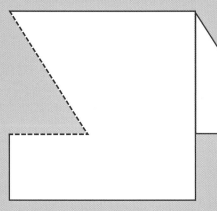

You have made an octagon. Try making a tessellating pattern with your octagon.

2) Find a way to cut a triangle from one side of the square so that when you stick it on the other side, you make a hexagon.

Check that your shape tessellates.

Make sure the shapes don't overlap as you stick them together, or your new shape won't tessellate.

3) Find a different shape (NOT a triangle) to cut from one side of a square and stick on another side so that you make an octagon.

   Check that your shape tessellates.

4) By cutting only ONE shape from the side of a square and sticking it on another side, make a 10-sided shape that tessellates.

   Investigate how many ways you can do this.

Jolly good show everybody! I wonder if I can get to my front door without stepping on any cracks?

Da Vinci files

- Use Huxley's method to make some other tessellating shapes from squares. Draw the tessellating patterns.

  Write down the number of sides each shape has.

- How many of your tessellating shapes have an odd number of sides? How many have an even number?

- Design a driveway for Prince Barrington with tessellating shapes.

  Put 5 stones in each row of the path.

  Use stones with different numbers of sides for each row.

Digital watch

Time: A lazy afternoon
Place: Victor's lab

Victor has been developing a new Daydream virus to cause havoc in Dr Hood's HQ. But some of the virus has leaked out and infected everyone who enters Victor's lab.

Ah, Da Vinci, just look at my calculator! It makes pretty patterns and shapes, ja?

Shouldn't you be getting on with... erm... what was it again? Although, now you mention it, those patterns are pretty, aren't they?

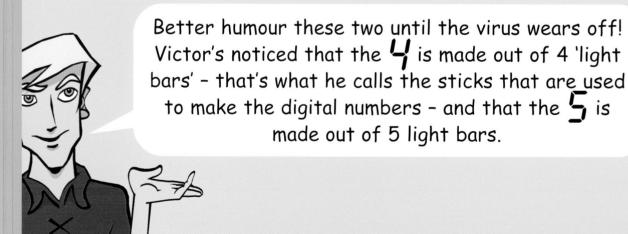

Better humour these two until the virus wears off! Victor's noticed that the **4** is made out of 4 'light bars' – that's what he calls the sticks that are used to make the digital numbers – and that the **5** is made out of 5 light bars.

1) Are any of the other digits made out of their own number of light bars?

2) Which digits use the same number of light bars as each other?

3) Which digit uses the most light bars?

4) Which digit uses the fewest light bars?

MM

Now, I'm interested in ze digits, I can't stop looking and counting! I'm looking for numbers zat use ze same number of light bars.

1) He knew that the digit **8** used 7 light bars.

He hunted for other numbers that used 7 light bars in total.

Here is one that he found: *12*

a) Find other numbers that use 7 light bars.

b) What is the largest number you can make that uses 7 light bars?

c) What is the smallest number you can make that uses 7 light bars?

2) Victor noticed that several numbers used 8 light bars in total. Here are two of them:

a) Find other numbers that use 8 light bars.

b) What is the largest number you can make using 8 light bars?

c) What is the smallest number you can make using 8 light bars?

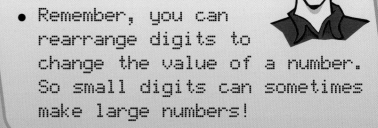

HUXLEY'S THINK TANK

- Remember, you can rearrange digits to change the value of a number. So small digits can sometimes make large numbers!

3) Victor did a calculation on his calculator. Here is the answer:

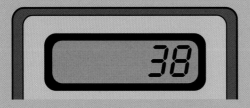

a) If the calculation was an addition, what might it have been?

Find at least 3 additions that give the answer 38.

b) If the calculation was a subtraction, what might it have been?

Find at least 3 subtractions that give the answer 38.

c) If the calculation was a multiplication, what might it have been?

How many multiplications can you find with the answer 38?

4) Victor noticed that the answer 38 used 12 light bars.

Can you find a calculation (addition, subtraction or multiplication) that gives a different answer using 12 light bars?

5) Victor did another calculation and the answer used 10 light bars.

a) Write 3 different numbers that the answer could be.

Make sure that at least one of them is a 3-digit number.

b) For each of your numbers:

- write an addition calculation that gives the number.

- write a subtraction calculation that gives the number.

- write a multiplication calculation that gives the number.

I've seen ze light... and ze virus works well, too!

Da Vinci files

- Victor looked at the time on his digital clock when he had completed the calculation and noticed that it used 14 light bars. What time might it have been?

Round and round and round...

Time: 8:30 a.m.
Place: Security office

The Museum is displaying the Police Force's world-famous collection of rare uniform buttons. Hilary Kumar has asked Inspector Pattern and Buster Crimes to check the security arrangements and their first job is to arrange the buttons in the square display cases where the security cameras are set up to catch any D.A.F.T. action.

Round buttons in square cases?

Don't worry, sir! I'll soon have the problem 'buttoned-up'!

TM

Some of the buttons in the collection are made out of shiny metal.

1) 18 shiny metal buttons are exactly the same as each other.

   Inspector Pattern wants to arrange these matching buttons in 3 equal rows.

   How many buttons should go in each row?

2) What other arrangements could she make with all 18 matching buttons so there are the same number of buttons in each row?

3) A friend gave her 2 more shiny buttons that matched the others exactly.

What arrangements could she make now?

Remember, I like to have the buttons arranged neatly in rows! Please make sure there is always more than 1 row.

There are black plastic buttons as well as shiny metal ones in the collection. I've started arranging the buttons to make squares where the number of buttons in each row is the same as the number of rows.

1) One square has 3 buttons in each row. How many buttons are there in the square altogether?

2) Another square has 25 buttons altogether. How many buttons are there in each row?

3) Inspector Pattern has 90 plastic buttons.

What different sizes of squares can she make with them?

4) Find a way of arranging the 90 plastic buttons in squares so that all of the 90 buttons are used.

You can make more than 1 square!

5) Now find a different way of arranging the 90 plastic buttons in squares so that all the buttons are used.

Remember, there should be at least 2 rows in each square.

HUXLEY'S THINK TANK

- Square arrangements mean the number of buttons in each row is the same as the number of rows.

  So 2 rows of 2 will make a square of 4 buttons.

  6 rows of 6 will make a square of 36 buttons.

- The numbers 4 and 36 are called square numbers because they make square arrangements.

Inspector Pattern started building some patterns of her own...

- She started with 1 shiny button.
  Then she added some plastic buttons
  to make a square.
  How many did she add?

- Then she added some more shiny buttons
  to make a bigger square.
  How many did she add this time?

- Then she added some more plastic buttons
  to make an even bigger square.
  How many did she add this time?

- How many shiny buttons will Inspector Pattern
  have to add to make the next square?

What do you notice about the number
of buttons I added each time
to make the square bigger?

I believe I will always have to add
an odd number of buttons to 1 square
to make the next size square.

Am I right?

How do you know?

Square-count cat?

Time: About 10 a.m.
Place: Mrs Tiggles' front room

Mrs Tiggles is making a huge patchwork blanket for her cat, James Bond, by sewing together knitted squares. Inspector Pattern has dropped by to see her.

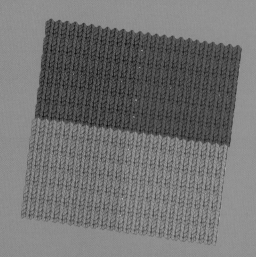

Look, I've done 4 squares since breakfast!

I beg to differ Mrs T – you've done more than that!

Why does Inspector Pattern think that there are more than 4 squares?

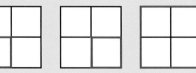

Well, there are these 4 small squares... and then there's the big square, too.

1) Mrs Tiggles added some more squares to her patchwork.

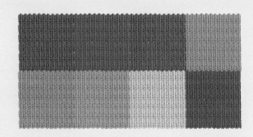

  a) How many small squares would Inspector Pattern find in this patchwork?

  b) How many big squares would she find?

  c) How many squares would Inspector Pattern find altogether?

2) Mrs Tiggles knitted on and added some more squares.

  a) How many small squares would Inspector Pattern find in the patchwork now?

  b) How many big squares would she find?

  c) How many squares would Inspector Pattern find altogether?

3) Mrs Tiggles knitted on and on.

How many squares would Inspector Pattern find altogether in the patchwork now?

HUXLEY'S THINK TANK

- Remember, you can count all the small squares first, then count the big ones.

While I'm knitting, Inspector Pattern has been jotting down the sizes of the patchwork and the number of squares in it.

This is what she's written:

Length of patchwork	2	3	4	5
Number of small squares	4	6	8	10
Number of big squares	1	2	3	4
Total number of squares	5	8	11	14

1) Look closely at the table.

a) What patterns can you see in the numbers?

b) How many SMALL squares do you think there will be altogether when the patchwork has a length of 6? Don't draw – just write your prediction.

c) How many BIG squares do you think there will be?

d) How many squares do you think there will be altogether when the patchwork has a length of 6?

e) Now check your predictions. Draw a patchwork with a length of 6 and count the number of squares. Did you predict correctly?

2) Mrs Tiggles' friend, Matilda, is also making a patchwork for her cat, Blofeld. She put her squares together in 3s.

How many squares are there altogether when her patchwork has a length of 3?

length: 3

3) Make a table for Matilda's patchwork.
You might want to draw patchworks with lengths of 4 and 5.

Length of patchwork	3	4	5
Number of small squares			
Number of medium squares			
Number of big squares			
Total number of squares			

4) How many squares will there be when the patchwork has a length of 6. Give an answer without drawing the patchwork.

5) How many squares will there be when the patchwork has a length of 7? Give an answer without drawing.

6) Draw patchworks and check your answers for lengths of 6 and 7.

7) How many squares will there be when Matilda's patchwork has a length of 10? Give an answer without drawing the patchwork.

Da Vinci files

- Jemima is also making a patchwork for her cat Moneypenny.

  She puts her squares together in 4s.

  Jemima's patchwork has 100 squares in it altogether.

  How long is it?

Time flies (if you throw your watch out of the window!)

Time: Morning has broken
Place: Army barracks

Two new recruits are arriving at the army
– Private Sloppy (PS) and Private Joker (PJ).

It's important we get everything on time, by Jove. I need to know that my recruits are following a tight schedule.

We'll need to lend the General a hand. I have a sneaky suspicion about these two ...

TM

Hmmm. Who do you think they might be working for? Let's try to find out more.

1) PJ takes 2 hours longer to travel to base than PS. Both leave home after 8 a.m. and arrive at the base at 4 p.m. They both leave home on the hour.

What times might they have left home? Work out all the possible answers.

Just keep adding 1 hour at a time.

2) The new recruits register. It takes PS 9 minutes and
PJ 15 minutes. Next, they both make a phone call home.

PS is on the phone 4 minutes less than PJ.
PS spends at least 5 minutes on the phone.

a) If PJ talks on the phone for 20 minutes, how
long does it take PS to register and phone?

b) What is the least time they could each spend
registering and phoning?

3) When they are shown to their rooms, they have
to unpack. Then, they make up their beds.

It takes PJ 3 times as long to make
up his bed as it does to unpack.

It takes PS twice as long to unpack
as to make up his bed.

a) If they both take 10 minutes to
unpack, how long does it take each
of them to make up their bed?

b) If they both take exactly 36 minutes to unpack and make up
their bed, how long does each recruit spend on each activity?

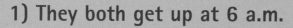

In the morning, the new recruits do the same jobs in the same order. Work out at what time they do each job.

1) They both get up at 6 a.m.

PJ takes 4 minutes longer to shower than PS. Both brush their teeth for 3 minutes.

PS took twice as long to dress as to shower. PJ took the same length of time to do both.

PJ made his bed in 3 minutes. This was half the time PS took.

They both spend 10 minutes preparing the room for inspection. PS spends at least 2 minutes in the shower.

a) What is the earliest they could each be ready?

HUXLEY'S THINK TANK

- You could work from how long PS spent in the shower.

b) How long does PS spend in the shower if they are both ready at the same time?

c) If they are both ready by 7 a.m., find all the possible times they could be ready.

d) For a special mission, they have to be ready at 5:12 a.m. exactly. If it takes PJ 9 minutes to dress, what time should they each get up to make sure they are ready in time?

Da Vinci files

Make up your own problem involving different lengths of time. Make sure that:

- you keep at least one of the lengths of time secret.

- one of your other times is a given length of time more or less than the missing length of time.

- you give either a start or finish time.

- there are at least 4 activities that have to be timed.

Ask a friend to solve your problem to check it works.

Just as I thought, General. Those two are D.A.F.T. agents in disguise!

Great Scott! How do you know?

I overheard PJ say that there are 3 kinds of people in this world – those that can count and those that can't!

Button holes for Victor

Time: A lazy evening
Place: Victor's lab

Victor Blastov owns several calculators. He uses them so much that some of the keys have fallen out of them.

It vos while I vos playing vis de calculator in my last mission zat I came up vis zeez ideas. See if you can match me vis your brilliance!

TM

Victor's blue calculator has lost these keys:

| 7 | 8 | 9 | × | ÷ |

1) Victor wanted to work out the sum 64 + 9 on this calculator.

Here is one way he could do it:

| 6 | 4 | + | 1 | 0 | – | 1 | = |

TM

Write down the keys to press for another way of getting the correct answer.

2) He then wanted to work out 53 + 19 on the calculator.

Here is one way he could do it:

| 5 | 3 | + | 1 | 0 | + | 5 | + | 4 | = |

Find another way of getting the correct answer using fewer key presses.

MM

1) Here is another addition Victor wants to do on the calculator:

54 + 29

a) Find at least 3 ways he could get the correct answer. Write down the keys he would press for each way you find.

b) Which of your ways uses the fewest number of key presses?

c) What is the smallest number of key presses Victor could use to get the correct answer?

2) This is a list of additions Victor wants to do on the calculator.

a) For each calculation, find at least 2 ways he could get the correct answer.

Write down the keys he would press for each way you find.

b) Which of the ways uses the fewest number of key presses?

56 + 9

45 + 18

63 + 29

36 + 48

29 + 29

3) Here is another list of calculations Victor wants to do. This time they are subtractions.

43 − 9
61 − 19
55 − 18
60 − 27

a) For each calculation, find at least 2 ways he could get the correct answer.

Write down the keys he would press for each way you find.

b) Which of the ways uses the fewest number of key presses?

4) Victor also has a red calculator. It has some missing keys as well.

Help Victor sort out how to use it to do these calculations.

For each calculation, find the way that uses the fewest keys possible.

54 + 41
75 − 42
87 + 33

Vell done, if you have come up vis de solutions! Great minds sink alike, ja?

HUXLEY'S THINK TANK

- When you are adding or taking away numbers that are close to 10, 20, 30 and so on, you can add or subtract the nearest 10 and then adjust your answer.

Da Vinci files

Here are both of Victor's calculators.

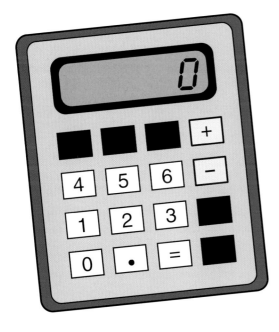

- How can he use his calculators to do these calculations?

- For each calculation, see if you can find a way on the blue calculator and a way on the red calculator.

- List the ways that you find. Don't forget to say which calculator you used!

54 + 19

65 − 32

70 + 34

35 − 17

Giggles at bedtime!

Time: Maryland's bedtime
Place: The Whitehouse bedroom

The president has been attacked by rogue numbers, which are sent to his computers. The numbers attack the computers' memory and cause the screens to show endless repeats of 'The Giggle Brothers' children's shows! How annoying is that?

We need a way to stop these numbers getting through. Yo, MT, how ya doin'?

Kinda fine, Buster C. I sure am lovin' these Giggle boys' shows! I ain't laughed so much in years!

Let's start by finding these missing numbers for Buster.

Using the inverse (opposite) calculation helps with some missing number calculations. Remember that addition and subtraction are inverses.

1) Take a look at these calculations and write the correct number for each one.

a) ☐ + 46 = 95

b) ☐ − 47 = 65

c) ☐ + 546 = 842

d) ☐ − 289 = 346

2) Buster remembers that some rogue numbers can be neutralised by changing them to numbers where the digits are all the same.

For example, you might change 645 to 777.

Work out what you need to add to or subtract from these numbers to change them to the safe number shown.

a) 645 is neutralised to 888.

b) 862 is neutralised to 444.

c) 193 is neutralised to 666.

d) 690 is neutralised to 555.

Explain how each one was done.

Palindromes might sort out these rogues!

HUXLEY'S THINK TANK

- Palindromes are numbers that are the same whether you write them backwards or forwards.

  For example, if you write 12321 backwards you get 12321, so 12321 is a palindrome. The numbers 474, 77 and 1064601 are also palindromes.

3) Which of these numbers are palindromes?

353   753537   58985   4040   4334   648648   865568

4) Write all the palindromes that are greater than 280 and less than 320.

5) Write all the palindromes that are greater than 4500 but less than 5300.

When these rogue numbers are dropped into my computer, they have to be neutralised by changing them into palindromes. Do ya catch my drift?

To work properly, palindromes must have the same number of digits as the rogue number.

However, each palindrome can be used once only, so you need all the possible ways to neutralise each number in case the rogue numbers appear more than once.

1) a) Using ADDITION, find all the ways to neutralise 68.

   b) Using SUBTRACTION, find all the ways to neutralise 68.

   c) How many ways are there to neutralise 68?

2) Use ADDITION and SUBTRACTION to find all the ways to neutralise 45. How many ways did you find?

3) Use ADDITION and SUBTRACTION to find all the ways to neutralise 59. How many ways did you find?

4) What do the answers from questions 1, 2 and 3 show?

5) Buster is excited. He says there will be 900 palindromes with 3 digits, so there will be 900 ways to neutralise each 3-digit rogue number.

   Is he right? Explain your answer.

When the team test palindromes on 3-digit rogue numbers, they find that:

- the palindromes must have the same number of digits.

- the sum of the digits in each number must be the same.

Further, if the rogue number is even, the palindrome is ODD and if the rogue number is odd, the palindrome is EVEN.

HUXLEY'S THINK TANK

- This example might help you.

  576 has 3 digits, so the digit sum is 5 + 7 + 6 = 18, and the number is even.

  Palindromes with a digit sum of 18 are 585, 666, 747, 828 and 909.

  Possible palindromes to neutralise are 585, 747 and 909. They all have 3 digits, a digit sum of 18 and are odd.

- Use the information from the team to find all the ways to neutralise 674 and 325. How many ways did you find?

- Keep trying different rogue numbers to see how many palindromes will neutralise them.

Can you find any patterns for the team so they know how many ways there are to neutralise different numbers?

That's a mighty shame! I guess the Giggle Brothers are on DVD...

Breaking news... world's chocolate reserves melting fast!

Time: Tea break
Place: Downing Street tea room

Hilary Kumar is making a speech on global warming and the effects on the world's economy at a conference next week. She's called Echo into her office to help her sort through the research data before putting together her presentation.

I heard that two-thirds of the world's chocolate supply will be exhausted by 2020.

I heard that eight-twelfths of the world's chocolate was going to disappear by 2020. That's far worse!

Echo dear, two-thirds and eight-twelfths are the same... still, it sounds like a confectionery disaster to me!

Let's look at some fractions to help Echo understand better.

You need seven 6 x 6 squares of paper. It might help if you quickly colour each square a different colour.

1) Fold one of the squares of paper in half. Then, cut the paper in half and write $\frac{1}{2}$ on each piece.

2) Fold one of the squares into 4 and cut along the folds. Write $\frac{1}{4}$ on each piece.

3) Fold another piece into 4, then fold it in half again. Cut along the folds and write $\frac{1}{8}$ on each piece.

4) Fold a piece into 3. Make sure there are the same number of squares on each piece. Cut along the folds and write $\frac{1}{3}$ on each piece.

5) Make and label $\frac{1}{6}$ ths with another piece of paper.

6) Now make and label $\frac{1}{12}$ ths.

7) Label the last piece of paper as '1 whole'.

8) Now check that all your pieces are accurate!

HUXLEY'S THINK TANK

- The pieces must each have the same area if they are the same fraction.
- Counting the squares on each piece is a good way to check that you are accurate.

I get the idea, perhaps with global warming two-thirds of the world's chocolate is going to melt?

1) It takes 2 halves to cover 1 whole.

1 whole · · · · · · · · 2 halves

We can write this as $1 = \frac{2}{2}$.

a) How many $\frac{1}{3}$ s are needed to cover 1 whole?

b) How many $\frac{1}{4}$ s are needed to cover 1 whole?

c) Use your fraction shapes to copy and complete this list:

$1 = \frac{2}{2}$ $1 = \frac{\square}{4}$ $1 = \frac{\square}{8}$

$1 = \frac{\square}{3}$ $1 = \frac{\square}{6}$ $1 = \frac{\square}{12}$

d) What rule could you use for making fractions that are worth a whole 1?

2) Now try matching the other fraction shapes to the $\frac{1}{2}$. Copy and complete the 2 sets.

What pattern can you see?

Fractions the same as $\frac{1}{2}$	Fractions that don't match $\frac{1}{2}$
$\frac{2}{4}$	$\frac{1}{3}$

What rule could you use for making fractions that are worth $\frac{1}{2}$?

MM 3) Now try matching the other fraction shapes to the $\frac{1}{3}$. Make a table like before and complete the 2 sets.

What rule could you use for making fractions that are worth $\frac{1}{3}$?

4) Now try matching the other fraction shapes to the $\frac{1}{4}$. Make a table and complete the 2 sets.

What rule could you use for making fractions that are worth $\frac{1}{4}$?

5) Can you think of a rule for finding fractions that are equivalent?

HUXLEY'S THINK TANK

- Fractions that are the same are called EQUIVALENT FRACTIONS.

Da Vinci files

- Produce an equivalent fraction chart for Echo by using the numbers 1 to 30 to make as many equivalent fractions as you can.

- Check that Echo will find your chart easy to understand and ask a friend to check that all your fractions are equivalents.

I need to plan my next eco-campaign. Save the polar ice caps or blocks of chocolate... blocks of chocolate or polar ice caps.... No contest is it, really?!

Mission Strategies

MISSION FILE 2:1

Use the pipes in a step by step way. Start with one piece of pipe and see what different lengths you can make by adding one more piece. Then see what lengths you can make by adding two more pieces and so on. Do this for different starting pieces. Look out for repeats!

For the final challenge, the set of 4 pipes that you made in the Main Mission could be a useful starting place for your set of 5 pipes.

MISSION FILE 2:2

It is usually quicker to match the corners of shapes when you are checking if they will tessellate. Make sure you draw the shapes exactly the same each time. Follow the lines on your paper or draw round a template. It is important to be accurate! When you are sticking the shapes together use sticky tape, not glue, because you don't want the shapes to overlap. This job can be easier if you have a friend to help you.

In the Da Vinci Files, try and design a driveway for Prince Barrington with 3-sided shapes in the first row, 4-sided shapes in the second row, 5-sided shapes in the third row, 6-sided shapes in the fourth row and so on.

MISSION FILE 2:3

You might like to use lolly sticks, matchsticks or straws to make the digital numbers. So in the Main Mission question 1, you could use 7 sticks to see what numbers you can make using 7 light bars.

In the Main Mission question 4, you could start by finding a few different numbers that each use 12 light bars. Some numbers may be easier to use than others.

MISSION FILE 2:4

Use your times tables to solve the problems in the Training Mission.

For the Main Mission, you may find it useful to jot down a list of the first 9 or 10 square numbers. Try different combinations of the square numbers to make the totals you need. Looking at their units digits will often be enough to see if they are going to add up to 90.

MISSION FILE 2:5

There are 3 sizes of squares you can find in the Main Mission question 3. Work systematically to make sure that you count them all – find all of the small squares first, then all of the medium-sized squares and then all of the big ones.

For the Main Mission, questions 4 and 5, look for patterns in the numbers in the table. These should help you predict the number of different-sized squares for longer patchworks.

MISSION FILE 2:6

It might be a good idea to practise working out time intervals before you tackle this mission. A lot of the work in this mission involves solving logic puzzles. Make a list of the activities that are timed in each problem and write next to the activity anything you can work out about how long it will take. One activity will take a fixed time and you can work out the others from that one. Be careful with PJ and PS – don't mix the two recruits up!

MISSION FILE 2:7

When you are looking for the way that uses fewest key presses it might be a way that you wouldn't normally use!

For example, to work out '62 – 9' in your head, you might well take away 10 and then add 1. That is a very efficient mental method.... but '62 – 10 + 1 =' uses 8 key presses and '62 – 5 – 4 =' only uses 7 key presses.

MISSION FILE 2:8

Addition is the inverse of subtraction and subtraction is the inverse of addition. That means you can solve '? + 35 = 91' by working out '91 – 35 = ?'. There should be a pattern to the answers in the Main Mission for questions 1 to 4. Check your work carefully if you can't find it.

MISSION FILE 2:9

Remember that fractions have the same area (size) but do not need to be the same shape. When you are looking for rules for each fraction, look for a relationship between the numerator and denominator of each fraction (that means the top and bottom numbers). Think what you would do to one to change it to the other, but only use multiplication and division! In the Da Vinci challenge, look for as many different types of fractions as you can – $\frac{1}{5}$th, $\frac{1}{6}$th, $\frac{1}{7}$th and so on.

The TASC Problem Solving Wheel

TASC: Thinking Actively in a Social Context

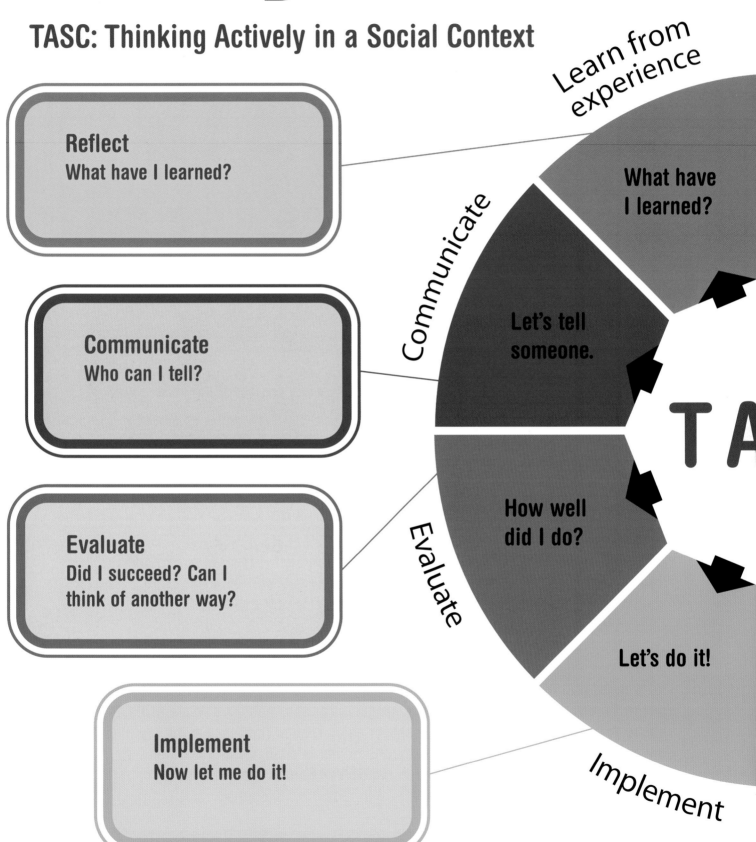

Reflect
What have I learned?

Communicate
Who can I tell?

Evaluate
Did I succeed? Can I think of another way?

Implement
Now let me do it!

Learn from experience

Communicate

What have I learned?

Let's tell someone.

How well did I do?

Evaluate

Let's do it!

Implement

TA

We can learn to be expert thinkers!

Gather/organise

What do I know about this?

Identify

What is the task?

Generate

How many ideas can I think of?

Decide

Which is the best idea?

S C

Gather and Organise
What do I already know about this?

Identify
What am I trying to do?

Generate
How many ways can I do this?

Decide
Which is the best way?

TASC: Thinking Actively in a Social Context © Belle Wallace 2004

nace

What is NACE?

NACE is a charity which was set up in 1984. It is an organisation that supports the teaching of 'more-able' pupils and helps all children find out what they are good at and to do their best.

What does NACE do?

NACE helps teachers by giving them advice, books, materials and training. Many teachers, headteachers, parents and governors join NACE. Members of NACE can use a special website which gives them useful advice, ideas and materials to help children to learn.

NACE helps thousands of schools and teachers every year. It also helps teachers and children in other countries, such as America and China.

How will this book help me?

Brain Academy Supermaths books challenge and help you to become better at learning and a better mathematician by:
- Thinking of and testing different solutions to problems
- Making connections to what you already know
- Making mistakes and learning from them
- Working with your teacher, by yourself and with others
- Expecting you to get better and to go on to the next book
- Learning skills which you can use in other subjects and out of school

We hope that you enjoy the books!

Write to **RISING STARS** and let us know how the books helped you to learn and what you would like to see in the next books.

Rising Stars UK Ltd, 22 Grafton Street, London W1S 4EX